I Ain't Gonna Paint No More!

I Ain't Gonna Paint No More!

Karen Beaumont

ILLUSTRATED BY David Catrow

SCHOLASTIC INC.

New York Toronto London Auckland Sydney
Mexico City New Delhi Hong Kong Buenos Aires

One day my mama caught me
paintin' pictures on the floor
and the ceiling
and the walls
and the curtains
and the door,
and I heard my mama holler
like I never did before...

"YA AIN'T A-GONNA PAINT NO MORE!"

I ain't gonna paint no more, no more,
I ain't gonna paint no more.

That's what I say...
but there ain't no way
that I ain't gonna paint no more.

So I take some red
and I paint my...

HEAD!

Now I ain't gonna paint no more.

Aw, what the heck!
Gonna paint my...

NECK!

Now I ain't gonna paint no more.

Still, I just can't rest
till I paint my...

CHEST!

Now I ain't gonna paint no more.

Guess there ain't no harm
if I paint my...

ARM!

Now I ain't gonna paint no more.

I ain't gonna paint no more, no more,
I ain't gonna paint no more.

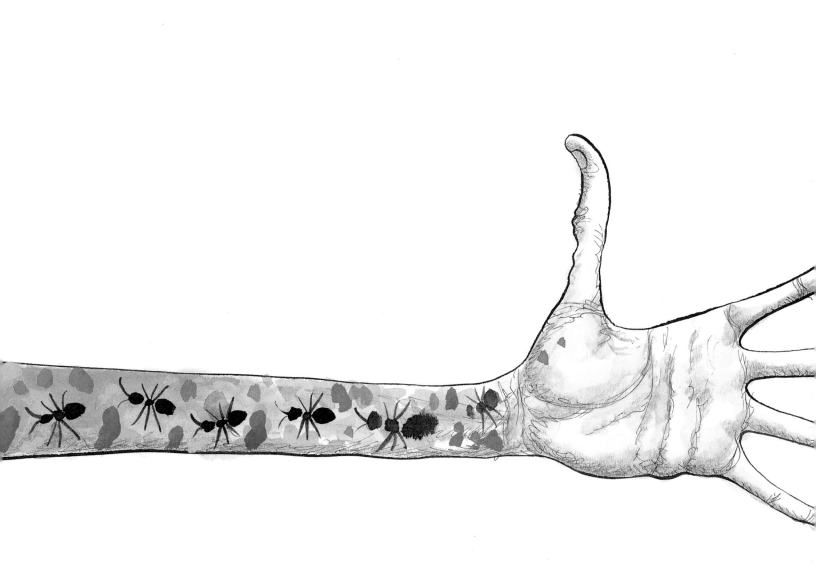

But I just can't stand
not to paint my...

HAND!

Now I ain't gonna paint no more.

Then I see some black
so I paint my...

BACK!

Now I ain't gonna paint no more.

Like an Easter egg,
gonna paint my...

LEG!

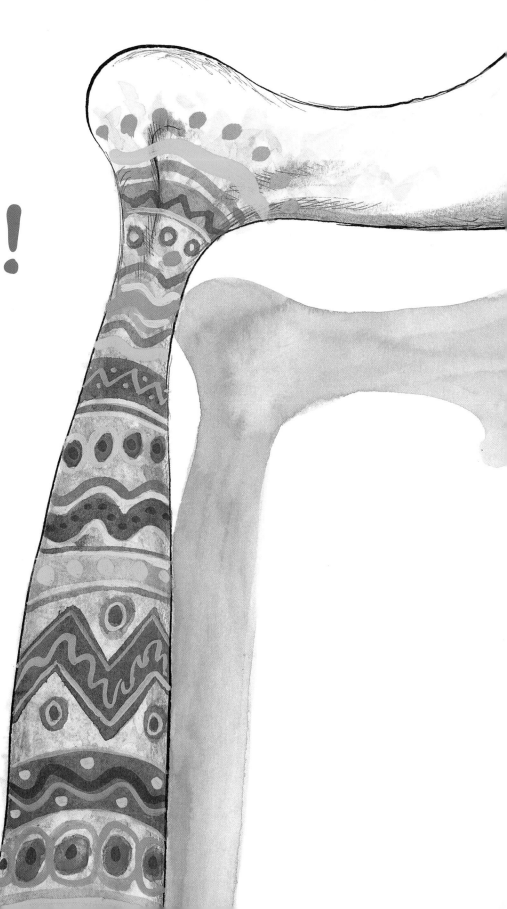

Now I ain't gonna paint no more.

Still, I ain't complete
till I paint my…

FEET!

Now I ain't gonna paint no more.

I ain't gonna paint no more, no more,
I ain't gonna paint no more.

But I'm such a nut,
gonna paint my—

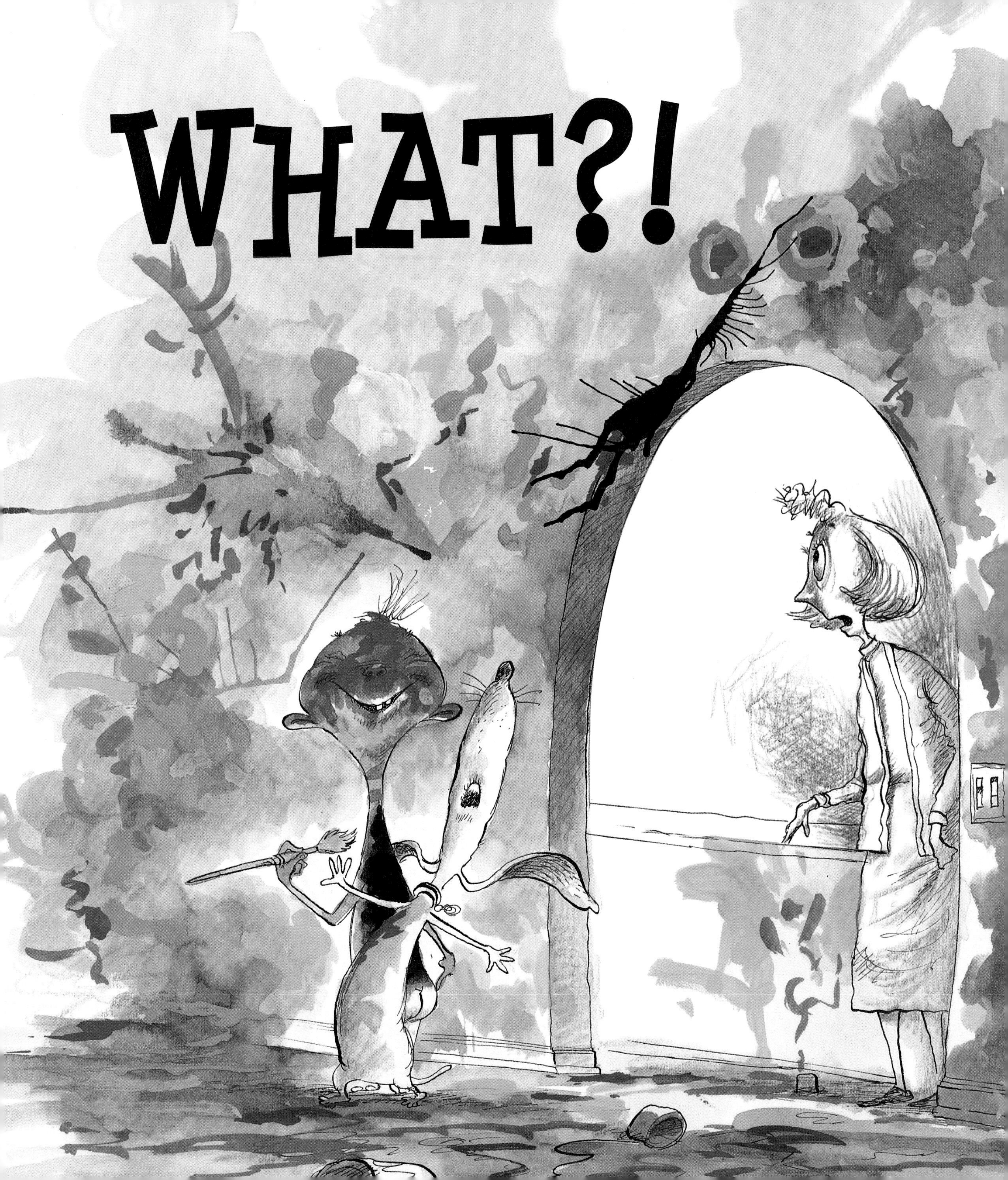
WHAT?!

Y'all don't faint...
'cause there ain't no paint!

So I ain't gonna paint no more!

For my beautiful daughters, Nicolyn and Christina,
who color my world with love—K. B.

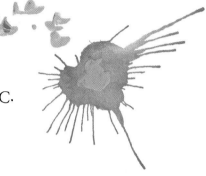

For Hillary, with love
Your greatest gifts are yet to be discovered—D. C.

ISBN-13: 978-0-439-92997-4
ISBN-10: 0-439-92997-0

Text copyright © 2005 by Karen Beaumont.
Illustrations copyright © 2005 by David Catrow. All rights reserved.
Published by Scholastic Inc., 557 Broadway, New York, NY 10012, by arrangement
with Harcourt, Inc. SCHOLASTIC and associated logos are trademarks and/or
registered trademarks of Scholastic Inc.

12 11 10 9 8 7 6 5 4 3 2   7 8 9 10 11 12/0

Printed in the U.S.A.   40

First Scholastic printing, February 2007

The illustrations in this book were done in ink and paint.

The display lettering was created by Jane Dill.

The text type was set in Garamouche.

Production supervision by Ginger Boyer

Designed by Judythe Sieck